Write & Burn Journal

Write it - Burn it - Release it

Write & Burn Journal

Write it - Burn it - Release it

SUNNY DAWN JOHNSTON

WRITE & BURN JOURNAL

Write it – Burn it – Release it

Copyright © 2018
By Sunny Dawn Johnston

Cover Design by Graphic Designer Kris Voelker
Edited by Deb McGowan
Formatted for Print by Shanda Trofe

For permission requests, write to the publisher:
SDJ Productions
4640 W. Redfield Road
Glendale, AZ 85306

www.sunnydawnjohnston.com

ISBN-13: 978-0-9961389-7-0

Printed in the United States of America.

Introduction

Have you ever heard of the Write and Burn process? You may have heard of Julia Cameron's "Morning Pages" ritual, that invites you to journal stream of consciousness thoughts for ten minutes each morning. It's a great way to get the funk and the junk out of your subconscious so you are more capable of being creative, intentional and free. Write and Burn, is similar, but different. It invites you to get honest with the feelings that don't feel good ... so honest that you are willing to move them out of your head and heart and onto paper. It is an extremely powerful process that I have been doing for years. I find it so helpful that I suggest it to about 90% of my clients at one time or another.

Writing to heal is scientifically proven. I knew I always felt better after I had written in my journal, especially the painful yucky stuff, but I didn't know there was "real" science that backed up what I felt. Not until I read an article about James W. Pennebaker, a psychology professor. He became deeply interested in the physical and mental benefits of what he called self-disclosure and created an experiment to test out his theory. He gathered a group of students who were asked to write about their own traumatic experiences for 20 minutes, on three consecutive days. Serving as a control group were an equal number of students asked to write about unimportant matters.

The results showed that there was a marked difference between the two groups in terms of the impact of the writing exercise. In those who had written of trivial matters, there was no change either in their physical or mental health. In contrast, those who had written about traumatic experiences showed a marked strengthening of their immune system, decreased visits to the doctor and significant increases in psychological well-being. These findings were measured using physiological markers, behavioral markers and self-reporting. In another study in the 1990s of people with AIDS, those who wrote about their diagnosis and how it had affected their lives experienced a beneficial increase in white blood cell counts and a drop in their viral loads.

How to Use the Write & Burn Journal

This is a simple journal to do all of your writing and burning. It is not meant for your regular daily journaling, gratitude lists or dreams and desires. This is for the YUCK. This is for the pain and anger and resentment and jealousy. This is for all those feelings of insecurity that hold you back in ways that you may just be discovering. This journal is a safe place to write all your pain, your problems, your challenges and yes, even your hates.

It is a place to come to once a day or once a week … whenever you have emotions that you want to release from your mind and body in a healthy way. It is so much better to come here than yelling and screaming, stuffing the body with food and alcohol, letting the critical voice take over or simply ignoring and denying the feelings.

The intention of this Write & Burn Journal is for you to write out your pain, tear it out (yes, tear the pages out of this book) and burn it. This journal is meant to be used in that fashion. Not to hold onto the words and keep by your bedside to burn at the very end. No, it is meant for you to write, tear out and burn – each and every time you make an entry. So basically, this journal should always have only blank pages in it when you complete the process. Each time you write, tear out the pages and burn it. Don't leave any energy sitting in this journal. It is a journal of release.

The Write & Burn Journal is a safe place for you to release. It's a place for you to get honest with yourself and your pain. A place for you to allow yourself complete freedom to write whatever you want. No one else but you will ever see it, so swear and curse if you feel the need and write down *everything* that you feel about the person or the situation that is affecting you. Write about *why* you feel the way you do … even if it doesn't make sense.

Do your best not to feel any shame or guilt about what you write – you are allowed to express your emotions in any way that leads to healing. Don't suppress or deny the way you feel, instead get it all out on paper. There are no judges here in this journal. There truly is no right or wrong way to do this … well, I guess there could be one wrong way. That would be not doing it. Not writing & burning. Just keep those feelings and emotions stored within and letting them steal your life away from you, negative thought-by-thought and unhealthy action-by-action.

Steps to Writing & Burning

1. Find a quiet spot where you are free from distractions. Turn your cell phone off. Get away from your computer. This is your time to RELEASE AND HEAL.

2. You may want to begin with a statement, intention or prayer asking to help you in clearing any negative emotions you have within your mind, body or spirit. Is there someone in your life (alive or deceased) that you have negative feelings toward? It could be an ex-lover, parent, spouse or colleague – anybody that conjures up negative feelings. Perhaps it is an experience that you need to let go of to move forward in your life. Whatever it is, bring it to mind as you make this statement of release.

3. Begin to write. Visualize the energy of pain, anger, hate, jealousy … whatever it is you feel within … imagine it. Imagine your emotions flowing down your arm and into the pages of this journal. Imagine the paper storing all the emotional energy that has felt stuck in you. It is literally taking your pain from your physical body and transferring it onto the paper and into this journal.

4. Write until your hand stops. Don't hold back. Don't stop what comes to your mind. This letter is for you. No one else has to see it. Proper grammar, sentence structure and punctuation are not important. Don't worry about editing your writing. Just keep going until you feel the pain subsiding and you feel as though your writing is complete. No need to go back and edit.

5. Ask if everything is clear. If yes, complete this exercise by writing down ***"My intention is that all of this is released energetically, emotionally, physically, and spiritually from me and from all generations past, present and future for the highest and greatest good of all."*** If it isn't feeling clear, keep writing.

6. Once complete, tear out the papers, and as you do, be aware of the energy you are feeling in your mind, heart and body. Notice how it feels to tear the pages out of the journal. Imagine you are CHOOSING now, to finally release them, once and for all.

7. Now it's time to BURN them baby!! No need to ever read them again. Just let them go. Go outside and make sure you have a safe receptacle that you can drop a burning piece of paper into, checking that the area around it will also be safe from the flames. Hold the letter over the receptacle and light one corner with a match or lighter. (Of course, you could also use a fireplace, wood bring stove or campfire to burn your pages in as well.)

8. Make a final statement of release. Before you just throw the paper in the fire, think about an intention of release you may want to say aloud – a statement of completion or letting go. As the paper begins to burn, I like to say something to the effect of, ***"I now release burn and clear all of this negativity to the Universe and ask that it be transmuted and transformed into Light."*** As you watch the page or pages burn, let all that anger and hate go with it. See and feel the energy transmuting with the support of the fire.

9. When your pages are completely burned, I like to say a special "Thank you and so it is" to the Universe. Since everything and everyone in the Universe is energetically connected, every time you do an exercise like this you are not only healing yourself but having an effect on others as well.

10. Lastly, pick up your pretty journal now. Write down five things that you appreciate in this moment. They can be anything and do not have to be associated with the person or experience that you have just written about. We do this to bring in something positive to the space that was cleared so that the same energy that was held there previously doesn't automatically get attracted back in and take up residence there again. By doing this, we consciously and intentionally replace that old negative energy with light and love and truth. **THIS IS A HUGE piece of Writing & Burning that gets missed, so please don't stop before this IMPORTANT step!**

Now my friend, it's time to do it. It's time to write it, release it, burn it and HEAL IT!!!!! The power YOU have to heal yourself is incredible. This is an experience that takes no money, no one outside of you, and just this simple journal, a pen and a lighter. That's it. It doesn't take a ton of time, but IT CAN BE one of the most healing exercises you can do on your own.

I'll be there in Spirit, holding your hand by the fire, as you release the old and step into the new.

You deserve the freedom. You deserve to live a life of light and love and happiness. It's your time to shine. Claim it now!

Love & Light,
Sunny Dawn Johnston

Journal

WRITE IT ~ BURN IT ~ RELEASE IT

WRITE IT ~ BURN IT ~ RELEASE IT

WRITE IT ~ BURN IT ~ RELEASE IT

WRITE IT ~ BURN IT ~ RELEASE IT

WRITE IT ~ BURN IT ~ RELEASE IT

WRITE IT ~ BURN IT ~ RELEASE IT

WRITE IT ~ BURN IT ~ RELEASE IT

WRITE IT ~ BURN IT ~ RELEASE IT

WRITE IT ~ BURN IT ~ RELEASE IT

WRITE IT ~ BURN IT ~ RELEASE IT

WRITE & BURN JOURNAL

WRITE IT ~ BURN IT ~ RELEASE IT

WRITE IT ~ BURN IT ~ RELEASE IT

WRITE IT ~ BURN IT ~ RELEASE IT

WRITE IT ~ BURN IT ~ RELEASE IT

WRITE IT ~ BURN IT ~ RELEASE IT

WRITE IT ~ BURN IT ~ RELEASE IT

WRITE IT ~ BURN IT ~ RELEASE IT

WRITE IT ~ BURN IT ~ RELEASE IT

WRITE IT ~ BURN IT ~ RELEASE IT

WRITE IT ~ BURN IT ~ RELEASE IT

WRITE IT ~ BURN IT ~ RELEASE IT

WRITE IT ~ BURN IT ~ RELEASE IT

WRITE IT ~ BURN IT ~ RELEASE IT

WRITE IT ~ BURN IT ~ RELEASE IT

WRITE IT ~ BURN IT ~ RELEASE IT

WRITE IT ~ BURN IT ~ RELEASE IT

WRITE IT ~ BURN IT ~ RELEASE IT

WRITE & BURN JOURNAL

WRITE IT ~ BURN IT ~ RELEASE IT

WRITE IT ~ BURN IT ~ RELEASE IT

WRITE IT ~ BURN IT ~ RELEASE IT

WRITE IT ~ BURN IT ~ RELEASE IT

WRITE & BURN JOURNAL

About the Author

Sunny Dawn Johnston is a world-renowned inspirational speaker, spiritual teacher, and psychic medium. She's the author of twenty books, including her two flagship bestsellers, ***Invoking the Archangels*** and ***The Love Never Ends***, which have become the cornerstones for many of her keynote topics such as intuition, mediumship, and the angelic realm.

Sunny's community of devoted clients and students expands the globe, and through her courses, private sessions, and live events, Sunny has touched the lives of thousands, both online and in-person. Her clients best know Sunny for her infinite, unconditional love and lack of judgment as she prides herself on always coming from a place of integrity, both in life and in her work.

Sunny helps people **connect with their heart** and **release the things that hold them back** from being their greatest version of themselves. Combining the ***unconditional love*** of a mother and the ***tell-it-like-it-is honesty*** of a best friend, Sunny helps people move into a higher vibration of living … *and* a higher vibration of **Being**. Using her spiritual and intuitive gifts, she shines a light on the areas of lack, fear, insecurity and sometimes … *B***S***!* Sunny feels strongly that at the heart of these issues is a lack of ***Self-Love***. By reflecting the **true nature** of her clients back to them – **which *IS* Love** – they can experience, and then allow in that unconditional love, and begin to heal themselves.

Sunny's latest endeavor, ***SDJ Productions,*** has expanded her beyond writing and speaking events and into publishing and producing. Her latest projects include two multi-author compilations, ***365 Days of Angel Prayers*** and ***111 Morning Meditations,*** with many more in the works.

In her spare time, Sunny is actively involved in the spiritual community and volunteers as a psychic investigator for the international organization **FIND ME**. This is a not-for-profit organization of Psychic, Investigative, and Canine Search & Rescue (SAR) volunteers working together to provide leads to law enforcement and families of missing persons and homicide.

Sunny resides in Glendale, Arizona surrounded by a loving family and close friends. She believes in maintaining a healthy mix of work and play and encourages harmony in all areas of life.

To learn more about Sunny's work, please **visit her website:** www.sunnydawnjohnston.com

And connect with her in her **private Facebook group:** www.facebook.com/groups/SDJCommunity.

Additionally, Sunny invites you to join her virtual community *Soul Food with Sunny*, a membership site where you'll gain access to her 18 years of teachings, including her online courses and all her best content. https://soulfoodwithsunny.com/join/

Made in the USA
San Bernardino, CA
03 September 2018